DILBERT™

A Treasury of Sunday Strips:
Version 00

Other DILBERT books from Boxtree

Random Acts of Management
ISBN: 0 7522 7174 1

Dilbert Gives You the Business
ISBN: 0 7522 2394 1

Don't Step in the Leadership
ISBN: 0 7522 2389 5

Journey to Cubeville
ISBN: 0 7522 2384 4

I'm Not Anti-Business, I'm Anti-Idiot
ISBN: 0 7522 2379 8

Seven Years of Highly Defective People
ISBN: 0 7522 2407 7

Casual Day Has Gone Too Far
ISBN: 0 7522 1119 6

Fugitive from the Cubicle Police
ISBN: 0 7522 2431 X

Still Pumped from Using the Mouse
ISBN: 0 7522 2265 1

It's Obvious You Won't Survive by Your Wits Alone
ISBN: 0 7522 0201 4

Bring Me the Head of Willy the Mailboy!
ISBN: 0 7522 0136 0

Shave the Whales
ISBN: 0 7522 0849 7

Always Postpone Meetings with Time-Wasting Morons
ISBN: 0 7522 0854 3

DILBERT™

A Treasury of Sunday Strips: Version 00 by SCOTT ADAMS

B□XTREE

First published 2000 by Andrews McMeel Publishing, an Andrews McMeel Universal company, 4520 Main Street, Kansas City, Missouri 64111, USA

This edition published 2000 by Boxtree
an imprint of Pan Macmillan Ltd
Pan Macmillan, 20 New Wharf Road, London N1 9RR
Basingstoke and Oxford

www.macmillan.com

Associated companies throughout the world

ISBN 0 7522 7232 2

9 8 7 6 5

A CIP catalogue record for this book is available from
the British Library.

Printed by The Bath Press, Bath

What the heck is a tinial and why do we need one?

Introduction

Have you ever noticed that crazy people don't think they're crazy? I'm talking about the run-of-the-mill wackos who populate your day. They think they're "quirky" or "high maintenance" or "perfectionists," but they rarely realize they are nuts. This got me to thinking, what if I'm nuts and I don't know it?

I started a list of all the things I do that could be construed as crazy by an unkind observer. Number one on the list is "creating a list of all the things I do that could be construed as crazy by an unkind observer." Number two was wondering if writing "number one" is redundant, since "one" is obviously a number. Number three, or as I call it now, just "three," was overanalyzing everything. Soon I had over forty items that were about the list itself. I decided those don't count.

Sometimes I ask questions and then I don't listen to the answers. It's not entirely my fault. If I ask a simple question and someone launches into a background story with charts and graphs and samples of DNA, I start thinking about other things. Sometimes I get hungry and wander away. That probably looks crazy.

For five years I couldn't sleep if I lay on my left side. It felt like my guts weren't in the right place. It didn't hurt, it just felt weird knowing my internal organs might not be where they belonged. When I lay on my other side everything was fine. I don't know what changed, but now both sides work and my guts feel okay. I credit my spleen for fixing the problem because I don't know what else it's supposed to do and it rarely gets credit.

I'm a vegetarian. Some people think that's crazy. Every now and then a slow-witted carnivore will engage me in a philosophical debate on the question of whether humans are meant to eat meat. I point out that a live cow makes a lion salivate, whereas a human just wants to say "moo" and see if the cow responds. I suppose if you were really, really, hungry, a cow might make you salivate, too. But by then you'd be willing to eat your sneakers, your relatives, dirt, and just about anything else. If you were meant to eat cows, you'd see ol' Bessie in a pasture and think how satisfying it would be to tackle her from behind and start gnawing on her thigh. All of my arguments make perfect sense to me, but other people just shake their heads and walk away muttering.

I also have a habit of changing the subject without warning. This book is full of Sunday-sized color cartoons. Most people think it's my best work. I think they're crazy, but only in general—not on that specific point. I hope you like it.

Speaking of crazy, it's not too late to join Dogbert's New Ruling Class (DNRC) and be a part of the elite when Dogbert conquers the world and makes everyone else our domestic servants. All you have to do is sign up for the totally free *Dilbert* newsletter that comes out whenever I feel like it, usually four times a year.

To subscribe, send a blank E-mail to dilbert-text-on@list.unitedmedia.com.
To unsubscribe, send a blank E-mail to dilbert-off@list.unitedmedia.com.
If you have problems with the automated subscription method, write to newsletter@united-media.com.

You can also subscribe via snail mail:

Dilbert Mailing List
United Media
200 Madison Ave.
New York, NY 10016

Sometimes the sun makes me sneeze, but that's a fascinating story for another day.

S.Adams

Scott Adams

40

42

54

56

58

77

88

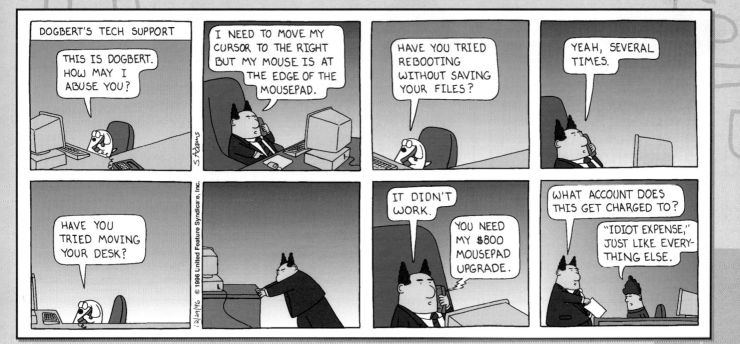

123

124

126

128

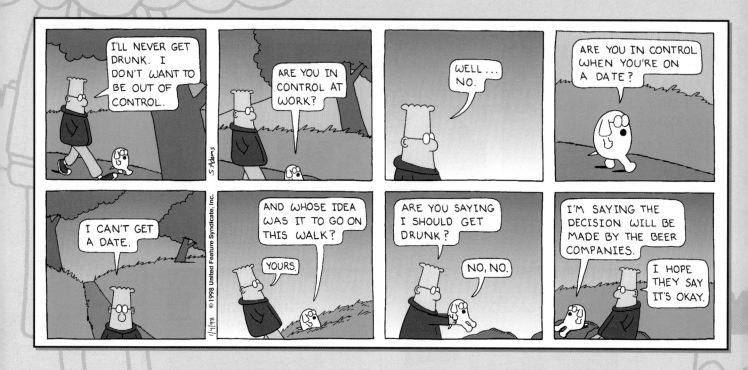

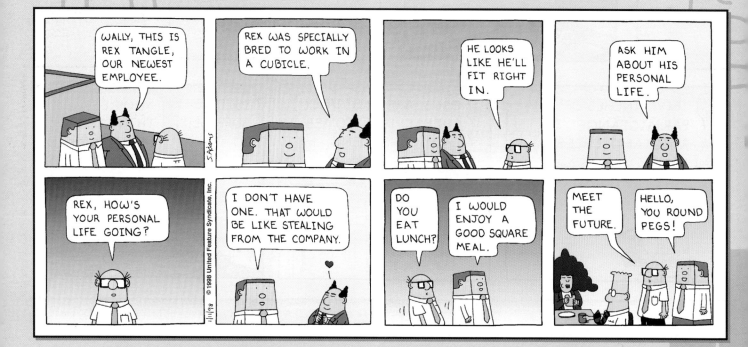

144

CATBERT: EVIL H.R. DIRECTOR

YOU LOOK STRESSED OUT, ALICE.

I COULD FIX THAT BY BECOMING A CHAMPION FOR IMPROVEMENTS IN THE WORKPLACE.

OR I COULD GIVE YOU A LITTLE BOOKLET CALLED "STRESS NO MORE."

HMM... I WONDER WHICH WAY IS BEST.

"STRESS IS YOUR BODY'S WAY OF SAYING..."

"... YOU HAVEN'T WORKED ENOUGH UNPAID OVERTIME."

I'VE NEVER SEEN A WOMAN'S FOREHEAD IGNITE HER HAIR BEFORE.

166

173

174

179

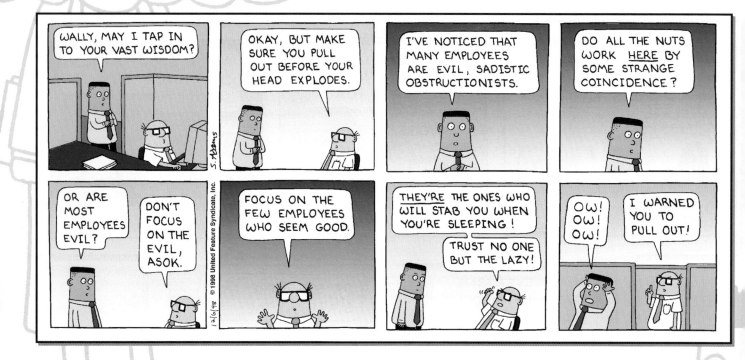

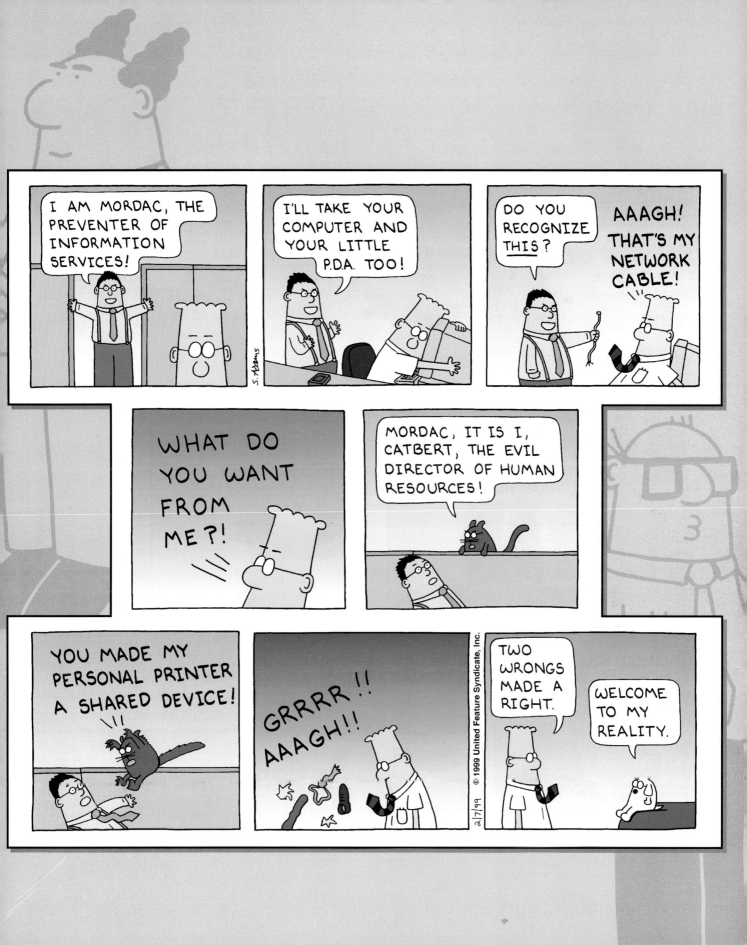

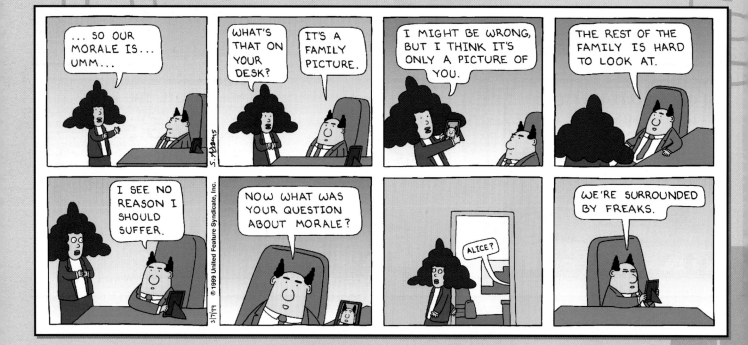

191

211

218